Sal Takes Charge

Matt Sims

High Noon Books
Novato, California

D1290295

Editor: Susan Blackaby
Cover Illustration: James Watling
Interior Illustrations: Rick Hackney

International Standard Book Number: 1-57128-248-3

Set ISBN: 1-57128-244-0
Set ISBN-13: 978-1-57128-244-6

16 15 14 13
14 13 12 11 10 09 08

You'll enjoy all the High Noon Books. Write for a free full list of titles or visit our web site at www.HighNoonBooks.com.

Contents

We Meet Sal

A kid came to live at my house. He is from a large town in Spain. He will stay with us for a year. His name is Sal.

At first, Sal was so shy! It was hard to speak to him. He said

At first, Sal was so shy!

"hi" and "eat" and "hot" and "sleep." That was it!

We had a list of things to say to him. Our speech was loud and slow. At first, he did not know what we had said.

Sal will sleep in my room. I gave him some help with his things. It was a squeeze to fit his things in. But Sal did not bring a lot of stuff with him. He had a trunk. He had a back pack. And he had a flute in a case. I gave Sal the top bunk. He was glad.

Smoke!

Sal had been at our house for more than six weeks. He felt at home now. Sal was a lot of fun to be with. I was glad to have him with us.

Sal still did not speak much. But I think

he got the things we said.

Then, last week, Sal was put to the test. We got home at the same time. Sal rode the late bus. I had my bike. Sal went up the steps. Then I saw him stop and sniff the air.

"Smell," he said.

"What is it?" I said.

Then I saw him stop and sniff the air.

"I do not smell a thing."
But then I could smell
it, too.

"Smoke!" said Sal.

"The house is on
fire!" I said.

I Take a Chance

I ran up the steps. I went to turn the knob.

Sal held my arm to stop me.

"No!" he said. He knew it was not safe.

"I have to save my dog!" I said back.

"I have to save my dog," I said.

Sal felt the side of the house.

"No heat," he said.

"We have to go in," I said. "We have to get Pooch."

"A step," said Sal. "No more."

I went in the house. I gave a yell for Pooch to come. There was a haze in the air.

Pooch ran to me. We were set to leave when I saw the flute case. It was in the den on a bench. I ran three steps to get it. I got it and ran back to the porch.

9-1-1

Sal got his cell phone. He hit 9-1-1.

"This call is for a fire," he said. "I am at 133 West Pine Drive. My cell phone is 555-2336. It is the home of Mark Blake. My name

Sal got his cell phone. He hit 9-1-1.

is Sal. There is smoke in the house. I do not feel heat. I do not see flame."

There was a pause. Then Sal said, "Yes. We went in to get the dog. No one else is at home. We just got here. Yes. Go south on Bridge Road. It is the quick way. The street is a block past the park. We will wait. Thank you."

"The trucks are on the way," Sal said to me. "Take Pooch to the next yard. Keep her there. The sound of the trucks will be loud. It will scare Pooch when she hears them."

I did what Sal said to do.

Sal Takes Charge

Pooch had the shakes. I did, too! I was glad Sal was in charge. We went to the next yard to wait for the trucks.

Sal gave my mom a call at work. "Please get me Ann Blake," said Sal.

Pooch had the shakes. I did, too!

The switch board said Mom had left for the day.

Sal said thank you. Then he put in a call to Dad. "Please give me the voice mail for Mark Blake," said Sal. Sal had to wait for the beep. He bit his lip.

"Hi, Mark," said Sal. "It is Sal. I am home

with Mike. There is smoke in the house. We did not see flames. The trucks are on the way. And we did get Pooch out of the house. You come home quick. I think Ann is on the way home now. We will see you soon."

Good Job!

Sal hit "off" to end the call. He stuck the phone in his pack. "Are you OK, Mike?"

"Yes, I am fine," I said. "Wow, Sal. You did a good job!"

"Thanks," said Sal.

"I am glad Pooch is OK. And I am glad you got my flute. You think quick on your feet, Mike!"

"So do you!" I said.

Just then the trucks came up the street with a roar. Mom drove up, too.

By then, we saw smoke in the sky. The

*Just then the trucks came up the street
with a roar.*

fire was in the back of the house. A cop came to speak with us.

"Ms. Blake," said the cop. "The fire will be out soon. It is not too big. Thanks to your boy, we got here quick. Your boy did a good job. He kept his cool. You can be proud of him."

That made Mom

smile. "Thank you," she said. "I am proud of each of my boys."

High Frequency Words

been	have	the
both	hold	there
call	Ms.	to
cold	of	were
come	one	what
could	put	would
do	said	your
from	small	
give	some	